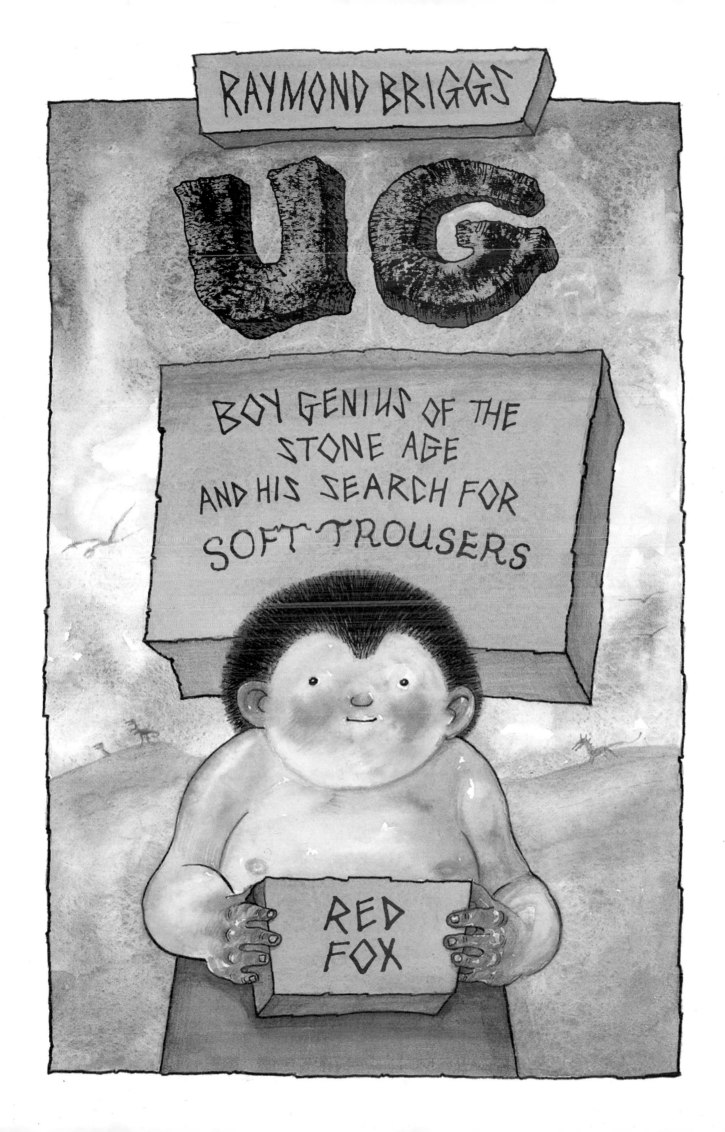

For
TOM *"Why do they have trees?"* BENJAMIN,
CLARE, SARAH, CONNIE, MATILDA & MILES

A RED FOX BOOK: 978 1 856 13054 7

First published in Great Britain by Jonathan Cape,
an imprint of Random House Children's Books

Jonathan Cape edition published 2001
Red Fox edition published 2002

3 5 7 9 10 8 6 4

Red Fox Books are published by Random House Children's Books,
61-63 Uxbridge Road, London W5 5SA,
a division of The Random House Group Ltd,
in Australia by Random House Australia (Pty) Ltd,
20 Alfred Street, Milsons Point, Sydney, NSW 2061, Australia,
in New Zealand by Random House New Zealand Ltd,
18 Poland Road, Glenfield, Auckland 10, New Zealand,
and in South Africa by Random House (Pty) Ltd,
Endulini, 5A Jubilee Road, Parktown 2193, South Africa

THE RANDOM HOUSE GROUP Limited Reg. No. 954009
www.**kids**at**randomhouse**.co.uk

A CIP catalogue record for this book is available from the British Library.

Printed in Singapore by Tien Wah Press (PTE) Ltd

② SUMMER HOLIDAY: (anachronism)
SUMMER HOLIDAYS WERE UNKNOWN
IN THE STONE AGE.
ALTHOUGH NO ONE WENT TO WORK,
THE STRUGGLE FOR SURVIVAL WAS SO HARD,
DUE TO THE STONY CONDITIONS, THE MUD
AND THE ENORMOUS NUMBER OF BUSHES
THAT THERE WAS LITTLE TIME LEFT
FOR HOLIDAYS. SO THEY WERE UNKNOWN.
    FURTHERMORE, THE CLIMATE WAS
COMPLETELY DIFFERENT TO THE PRESENT
DAY AND "SUMMER" WAS PROBABLY
UNKNOWN DUE TO THE CLIMATE
BEING COMPLETELY DIFFERENT.

③ BOOTS: (anachronism)
BOOTS WERE ALMOST UNKNOWN IN THE
STONE AGE. ANIMALS WITH LEATHERY
SKINS HAD NOT YET EVOLVED, AS ALL
THE ANIMALS WERE STILL PRE-HISTORIC
MONSTERS. SUCH BOOTS AS DID EXIST
WERE MADE OF STONE AND WERE
ALMOST AS UNCOMFORTABLE AS THE
STONE TROUSERS. SO THEY WERE NEVER
USED. CONSEQUENTLY, NO STONE AGE
BOOT HAS EVER BEEN FOUND, AND
OF COURSE, NEVER A PAIR.